GARY BARLOW — OPEN ROAD

Exclusive Distributors

International Music Publications Limited
Southend Road, Woodford Green, Essex IG8 8HN, England

International Music Publications Limited
25 Rue D'Hauteville, 75010 Paris, France

International Music Publications GmbH, Germany
Marstallstraße 8, D-80539 Munchen, Germany

Nuova Carish S.p.A.
Via Campania 12, 20098 San Giuliano Milanese, Milano, Italy

Danmusik
Vognmagergade 7, DK-1120 Copenhagen K, Denmark

Warner/Chappell Music Australia Pty Ltd.
3 Talavera Road, North Ryde, New South Wales 2113, Australia

Folio © 1997 International Music Publications Ltd
Southend Road, Woodford Green, Essex IG8 8HN

Music Transcribed by Barnes Music Engraving Ltd.,
East Sussex TN22 4HA

Printed by The Panda Group · Haverhill · Suffolk CB9 8PR · UK

Binding by ABS · Cambridge

Front Cover Photo Norman Watson

OPEN ROAD

GARY BARLOW

IT WAS A MONUMENTAL DAY IN POP HISTORY WHEN **GARY BARLOW** AND THE THREE OTHER MEMBERS OF **TAKE THAT** MADE THE MUTUAL AND RISKY DECISION TO DISBAND WHAT HAD BECOME THE POP SENSATION OF THE DECADE. IT WAS NOT ONE WHICH WAS TAKEN LIGHTLY, BUT ONE WHICH THE FOUR MEMBERS FELT WAS THE RIGHT ONE – IT WAS TIME TO MOVE ON FOR ALL OF THEM. THE REASONS FOR THE HEADLINE MAKING SPLIT WERE MADE CLEAR – THE HUGE UMBRELLA THAT WAS TAKE THAT MEANT THAT THE LADS HAD LITTLE TIME TO DEVELOP AS INDIVIDUALS AND WITH THE ARRIVAL OF NEWER AND YOUNGER BOY BANDS ON THE 'POP' SCENE THE FOUR SIMPLY FELT THAT, AS GARY FAMOUSLY SAID AT THE FAREWELL PRESS CONFERENCE "THE TIME HAD COME...".

HAVING ALREADY PENNED A STRING OF HITS WHILST IN TAKE THAT (**PRAY, A MILLION LOVE SONGS, BABE, EVERYTHING CHANGES, BACK FOR GOOD...**) IT WAS CLEAR FROM THE START THAT GARY POSSESSED THE PEDIGREE TO ENSURE THAT HIS NEW SOLO CAREER WOULD BE AS SUCCESSFUL AS HIS LAST. DURING THEIR FIVE YEAR REIGN AT THE TOP OF THE POP WORLD TAKE THAT WERE TO SELL OVER 10 MILLION ALBUMS WORLDWIDE AND NOTCHED UP AN INCREDIBLE **EIGHT UK NO 1'S**, A GOOD PROPORTION OF WHICH WERE GARY'S HANDIWORK. ALTHOUGH RESPECT FOR HIS SONGWRITING WAS GROWING RAPIDLY, IT WASN'T UNTIL THE 1995 RELEASE OF "BACK FOR GOOD" THAT GARY WAS TO BECOME ESTABLISHED AS ONE OF THE MOST PROLIFIC SONGWRITERS OF THE DECADE. THE SINGLE CATAPULTED THE GROUP TO AN INCREDIBLE FOUR WEEK STINT AT THE TOP OF THE UK CHARTS, AND EARNED THEM THEIR FIRST TOP TEN US ENTRY. THROUGHOUT THE GROUP'S CAREER GARY'S SONGWRITING BECAME INCREASINGLY SUCCESSFUL AND THIS WAS HIGHLIGHTED IN 1994 WHEN HE WAS AWARDED THE PRESTIGIOUS **IVOR NOVELLO AWARD** FOR "**BEST CONTEMPORARY SONG**" (FOR 'PRAY') AND THE TITLE "SONGWRITER OF THE YEAR", JOINING A ROLE CALL OF HONOUR WITH FORMER TITLE HOLDERS SUCH AS **ELTON JOHN, GEORGE MICHAEL, ANNIE LENNOX** AND **ERIC CLAPTON**. TWO YEARS ON HE WAS BACK, WINNING IN TWO CATEGORIES FOR HIS CRITICALLY ACCLAIMED **NUMBER ONE BALLAD "BACK FOR GOOD"** ("**BEST SONG MUSICALLY AND LYRICALLY**", "**THE PRS MOST PERFORMED WORK**") AND BEING **NOMINATED IN A FURTHER TWO** ("**THE BEST SELLING SONG**", "**INTERNATIONAL HIT OF THE YEAR**"). BUT EVEN AFTER THE HONOUR OF BEING PRESENTED WITH SUCH PRESTIGIOUS AWARDS GARY REMAINS HUMBLE. "THESE AWARDS ARE VOTED ON BY ONLY A FEW PEOPLE IN THE RECORD INDUSTRY, AND AT THE END OF THE DAY IT'S WHAT THE PUBLIC THINK. THEY'RE THE MOST IMPORTANT PART OF ALL OF THIS."

BUT WHEN GARY EMBARKED ON HIS SOLO CAREER IN JULY OF 1996, SURELY EVEN THOSE WHO PILED ON THE PLAUDITS DURING HIS TAKE THAT DAYS COULDN'T HAVE FORESEEN SUCH A BLISTERING START FOR HIM. HIS FIRST SOLO SINGLE RELEASE "**FOREVER LOVE**", A HUGE BALLAD FEATURING JUST ONE VOICE AND ONE PIANO, SHOT STRAIGHT INTO THE CHARTS AT NUMBER ONE. NINE MONTHS LATER (IN APRIL 1997), HIS SECOND SOLO SINGLE, THE HUGELY INFECTIOUS "**LOVE WON'T WAIT**", ALSO WENT STRAIGHT TO THE NUMBER ONE SPOT.

RED LETTER DAY, HOWEVER, WAS **MAY 26TH** OF THIS YEAR, WHEN GARY RELEASED HIS LONG-AWAITED DEBUT ALBUM "**OPEN ROAD**". IT WAS ANOTHER **NUMBER ONE!** ITS SUCCESS HAS ALSO VINDICATED GARY'S BRAVE DECISION TO RE-RECORD ALMOST THE ENTIRE ALBUM. ORIGINALLY, IT WAS SET TO BE RELEASED IN JUNE OF 1996. BUT ON A TRIP TO LA LAST YEAR, GARY MET **CLIVE DAVIS**, THE **HEAD OF ARISTA** RECORDS, GARY'S US RECORD LABEL. THE MEETING PROVED FORTUITOUS. "HE OFFERED ME THE CHANCE TO WORK WITH ALMOST WHOEVER I WANTED" EXPLAINS GARY. AND THAT OPENED UP A WHOLE NEW SET OF DOORS, AS HE WAS ABLE TO TEAM UP WITH RENOWNED WRITERS AND PRODUCERS SUCH AS **DAVID FOSTER** AND **DIANE WARREN** (**TONI BRAXTON**), **WALTER AFANASIEFF** (**MARIAH CAREY**) AND **TREVOR HORN** (**SEAL**). OF THE FINISHED RESULT, GARY DECLARES: "IT'S TEN TIMES BETTER THAN THE STUFF I'D DONE BEFORE - I'M GLAD I DELAYED IT "

THE ALBUM ITSELF SHOWS A DIVERSITY OF MUSICAL STYLES, WITH ACOUSTIC-BASED TRACKS, BALLADS AND UP-TEMPO NUMBERS. IT MARKS A DISTINCT CHANGE OF DIRECTION FOR GARY, ALMOST A 'BACK TO BASICS' APPROACH, AND CLEARLY SHOWS A MATURITY AND DEPTH OF FEELING BEYOND HIS YEARS. GARY HIMSELF DESCRIBES IT AS "A LYRICAL PROGRESSION FROM TAKE THAT. THIS IS THE MOST POSITIVE AND OPTIMISTIC MUSIC THAT I'VE WRITTEN - IT'S MORE ABOUT HAVING THINGS THAN LOSING THEM "

THE ALBUM'S TITLE ALSO REFLECTS THE EXTRAORDINARY PROGRESS THAT GARY HAS MADE IN HIS CAREER. HE HAS CERTAINLY COME A LONG WAY SINCE HIS TENTH BIRTHDAY WHEN HIS PARENTS BOUGHT HIM A KEYBOARD INSTEAD OF A BMX. GARY HAD EXHAUSTED ITS REPERTOIRE OF NOISES WITHIN WEEKS AND SOON PROGRESSED TO PLAYING A 'PROPER' HOME ORGAN WITH FOOT-PEDALS. BY THE AGE OF 12 HE WAS PLAYING WEEKENDS IN THE BAR AT A LABOUR CLUB IN NORTH WALES, AND AT 15 HAD WRITTEN HIS FIRST SONG. 16 SAW HIM LEAVE SCHOOL AND WORK AS A MUSICIAN AND AT 18 HE HAD A LIFE-CHANGING MEETING WITH A CERTAIN **NIGEL MARTIN-SMITH** WHO HAD "AN IDEA FOR A BAND". THE REST, AS THEY SAY, IS HISTORY. AND THE JOURNEY CONTINUES. GARY SEES THE RELEASE OF "**OPEN ROAD**" AS "ANOTHER BEGINNING. THE FIRST PHASE OF MY CAREER WAS WITH TAKE THAT AND THIS IS THE SECOND."

THE NEXT SIGNPOST ON THE ROAD IS GARY'S NEXT SINGLE, THE HAUNTING BALLAD "**SO HELP ME GIRL**", RELEASED ON **14TH JULY**. ORIGINALLY A COUNTRY CLASSIC, WRITTEN BY **HOWARD PERDEW** AND **ANDY SPOONER**, GARY'S VERSION IS PRODUCED BY DAVID FOSTER AND ESCHEWS THE COUNTRY AND WESTERN FLAVOUR FOR A MORE CONTEMPORARY FEEL TO TUG THE HEARTSTRINGS OF THE MOST HARDENED CITY DWELLER!

AND THE FUTURE BECKONS. WITH SUCH A SOLID START TO HIS SOLO RECORDING CAREER, GARY NOW LOOKS FORWARD TO CRACKING AMERICA AND PUTTING TOGETHER A LIVE BAND FOR DATES NEXT YEAR: "IT'S THAT RAW PERFORMANCE THAT IS WHAT IT'S ALL ABOUT FOR ME" HE ENTHUSES. BUT WHILE HE'S ONCE AGAIN IN DEMAND ALL OVER THE WORLD, HE ALSO HOPES TO FIT IN SOME TIME AT HOME TO WALK THE DOGS. AFTER ALL, IT'S THE SIMPLE THINGS THAT ARE WHAT LIFE IS ALL ABOUT....

LOVE WONT WAIT

WHEN I FIRST SAW YOUR FACE, I KNEW THAT I COULDN'T HESITATE, YOU SAID 'BABY DON'T GO TOO FAST', 'IF WE DO THEN IT MAY NOT LAST'. TIME WENT ON AND I WAITED FOR YOU, I DIDN'T KNOW WHAT ELSE I COULD DO, I THOUGHT THAT WE'D ALWAYS BE TOGETHER, YOU SAID 'HOLD ON IT JUST GETS BETTER'. AND I BELIEVED YOU, I KEPT HOLDING ON, YOU THINK THAT I COULD NEVER LEAVE YOU, YOU THINK I'M NOT THAT STRONG, YOU KNOW. LOVE WON'T WAIT (LOVE WON'T WAIT), FOREVER AND A DAY (LOVE WON'T WAIT), LOVE WAS LIVING A YEAR AND NOW, DON'T ASK ME HOW I KNOW (LOVE WON'T WAIT). HERE I AM WITH MY HEART ON MY SLEEVE, YOU SAID 'BABY, PUT YOUR TRUST IN ME', BUT I HAVE COME TO THE END OF THE LINE, AND YOU HAVE TAKEN UP ALL OF MY PRECIOUS TIME. I HOPED TO BE SOMETHING SPECIAL TO YOU, EVERYBODY'S SOMEBODY'S FOOL, WON'T BE YOUR FOOL, NO YOU GOT ME ALL WRONG, YOU WON'T KNOW WHAT YOU HAD 'TIL IT'S GONE. AND I BELIEVED YOU, I KEPT HOLDING ON, YOU THINK THAT I COULD NEVER LEAVE YOU, YOU THINK I'M NOT THAT STRONG, YOU KNOW. LOVE TAKES TIME (LOVE TAKES TIME), BUT YOU'VE BEEN TAKING TOO LONG (WAY TOO LONG), TIME NEVER WAITED FOR ANYONE, DON'T WAIT TOO LONG, OR I'LL BE GONE (LOVE WON'T WAIT). THERE WASN'T ANYTHING THAT I WOULD-N'T DO, YOU LED ME ON, YOU EVEN SAID 'I LOVE YOU', HOW CAN WE GO ON WHEN IT'S TEARING US APART, ARE YOU GOING TO BREAK MY HEART?. 'CAUSE I BELIEVED YOU, I KEPT HOLDING ON, YOU THINK THAT I COULD NEVER LEAVE YOU, YOU THINK I'M NOT THAT STRONG, YOU'RE WRONG. LOVE WON'T WAIT, LOVE WON'T WAIT, LOVE TAKES TIME (LOVE TAKES TIME), BUT YOU'VE BEEN TAKING TOO LONG (WAY TOO LONG), TIME NEVER WAITED FOR ANY-ONE, DON'T WAIT TOO LONG, OR I'LL BE GONE (LOVE WON'T WAIT). HOW MUCH LONGER CAN I WAIT FOR YOU, CAN I KEEP HOLDING ON, I'VE GOT TO BE STRONG, GOT TO SAY GOODBYE (LOVE WON'T WAIT). HOW MUCH LONGER CAN I WAIT FOR YOU, HESITATE FOR YOU, BABY?, I'VE GOT TO BE STRONG, GOT TO SAY GOODBYE. GOODBYE.

YOU SAY YOU NEED TWO ARMS TO HOLD YOU, YOU SAY YOU NEED A TOUCH THAT'S STRONG, ALL ALL ALL I CAN GIVE YOU, IS A LOVE TO LAST A LIFETIME LONG, HEAR WHAT I'M SAYING BABY. MY COMMITMENT MY COMMITMENT, MY COMMITMENT TO YOU, MY COMMITMENT MY COMMITMENT, IS TO LIVE TO LOVE YOU, I WILL HOLD YOU I WILL SHOW YOU, YOU CAN PUT YOUR FAITH IN ME, ALL OF MY LIFE I'LL BE ALL THAT YOU NEED. I'LL DRY EACH TEAR EACH TIME YOU CRY, I'LL LOVE YOU FROM THE HEART YES I WILL, I'LL I'LL I'LL NEVER LEAVE YOU, FOREVER YOU'LL BE SAFE WITHIN THESE ARMS, DON'T YOU HEAR WHAT I'M SAYING BABY. MY COMMITMENT MY COMMITMENT, MY COMMITMENT TO YOU, MY COMMITMENT MY COMMITMENT, IS TO LIVE TO LOVE YOU, I WILL HOLD YOU I WILL SHOW YOU, YOU CAN PUT YOUR FAITH IN ME, ALL OF MY LIFE I'LL BE ALL THAT YOU NEED. I WILL GIVE YOU STRENGTH, I'LL GIVE YOU FAITH, I'LL GIVE YOU ALL OF ME, THIS TIME THIS LOVE WON'T LET YOU DOWN, THIS TIME YOU CAN BELIEVE IN ME, LET MY LOVE BE THE ANSWER TO THE QUESTIONS IN YOUR HEART BABY, LOOK IN YOUR SOUL AND YOU'LL SEE, I'LL BE, ALL ALL ALL THAT YOU NEED, ALL ALL ALL THAT YOU NEED, THIS TIME I SWEAR YOU CAN BELIEVE, I'LL BE ALL ALL ALL THAT YOU NEED. MY COMMITMENT MY COMMITMENT, MY COMMITMENT TO YOU, MY COMMITMENT MY COMMITMENT, IS TO LIVE TO LOVE YOU, I WILL HOLD YOU I WILL SHOW YOU, YOU CAN PUT YOUR FAITH IN ME, ALL OF MY LIFE I'LL BE ALL THAT YOU NEED, COMMITMENT COMMITMENT MAKE YOUR COMMITMENT TO ME.

MY COMMITMENT

YOU COULD HAVE KISSED ME, LIKE THIS WASN'T GONNA LAST, KEPT ME FROM SAYING, SOMETHING I'LL NEVER TAKE BACK, YOU COULD'VE HELD ME LIKE THERE WAS NO CHANCE OF ME WAKING UP WHERE I AM, YOU COULD HAVE STOPPED SHORT OF EVERY DREAM I EVER HAD. SO HELP ME GIRL, YOU'VE GONE TOO FAR, IT'S WAY TOO LATE, TO SAVE MY HEART, THE WAY IT FEELS, EACH TIME WE TOUCH, I KNOW I'VE NEVER BEEN SO LOVED, AND I CAN'T HELP MYSELF, SO HELP ME GIRL. YOU HAD TO BE THERE WHEN THAT OLD SUN CAME UP, MAKING LAST NIGHT FEEL LIKE A VISION OF THINGS YET TO COME, YOU JUST HAD TO HOLD ME LIKE NOBODY ELSE, NOW LOOK WHAT YOU'VE GONE AND DONE, YOU HAD TO LOVE ME, 'TIL I JUST CAN'T GET ENOUGH. SO HELP ME GIRL, YOU'VE GONE TOO FAR, IT'S WAY TOO LATE, TO SAVE MY HEART, THE WAY IT FEELS, EACH TIME WE TOUCH, I KNOW I'VE NEVER BEEN SO LOVED, AND I CAN'T HELP MYSELF, SO HELP ME GIRL, AND I CAN'T HELP MYSELF, SO HELP ME GIRL

HANG ON IN THERE BABY

NOW THAT WE'VE CARESSED, A KISS SO WARM AND TENDER, I CAN'T WAIT 'TIL WE'VE REACHED, THAT SWEET MOMENT OF SURRENDER, WE'LL HEAR THE THUNDER ROAR, FEEL THE LIGHTNING STRIKE, AT A POINT WE BOTH DECIDED TO MEET, SAME TIME TONIGHT. HANG ON IN THERE BABY, HANG ON IN THERE DOLL, I'M GONNA GIVE YOU MORE, THAN YOU EVER DREAMED POSSIBLE. DON'T BE AFRAID BABY, OH NO, OH SWEET VIRGIN OF THE WORLD, WE CAN'T HELP BUT MAKE IT, 'CAUSE THERE'S TRUE LOVE BETWEEN US GIRL, SO LET US TOUCH THAT CLOUD, THAT EVERYONE DREAMS OF, OH WE'RE ALMOST THERE DARLING, WE'RE TRULY MAKING LOVE. HANG ON IN THERE BABY, PLEASE DON'T LET ME DOWN, PLEASE DON'T DESTROY, THIS NEW JOY WE'VE FOUND. WHAT'S THAT NOW BABY, WHAT'S THAT YOU SAY, SOMETHING'S EATIN' AT YOU, AND IT'S 'BOUT TO GET AWAY. DON'T FIGHT IT BABY, OPEN UP THE DOOR, 'CAUSE THAT'S THE KEY TO THE FREEDOM, THAT WE'VE BOTH BEEN WORKIN' FOR, LET IT GO BABY, LET IT GO HONEY, OH RIGHT THERE, RIGHT THERE, BABY DON'T YOU MOVE IT ANYWHERE, GO BABY, LET IT GO HONEY, OH RIGHT THERE, BABY DON'T YOU MOVE IT, DON'T YOU DARE. HANG ON IN THERE BABY, HANG ON IN THERE DOLL, I'M GONNA GIVE YOU MORE, THAN YOU EVER DREAMED POSSIBLE.

SO HELP ME GIRL

ARE YOU READY NOW

CAN WE SHARE TONIGHT THE YEARS WE'VE BEEN APART BABY, FROM THE TIME WE SAID GOODBYE UNTIL NOW, HOW THE NIGHTS WE LAUGHED AND LOVED STILL FEEL LIKE YESTERDAY, HOW I'M HOPING YOU STILL FEEL THE SAME. (SO) STRANGE WE'RE STANDING HERE AFTER ALL THIS TIME, STRANGE WHEN THE PRESENT AND THE PAST COLLIDES, MEMORIES OF OUR DAYS APART I FEEL THEY'RE FADING FAST, SILENCE FOR MY QUESTIONS HERE AT LAST. ARE YOU READY NOW FOR ME TO LOVE YOU, ARE YOU READY NOW TO GIVE THIS LOVE A TRY, ARE YOU READY NOW FOR ME TO GIVE YOU TRUST TO GIVE YOU TRUTH, ARE YOU READY NOW FOR ME. READY NOW FOR ME TO SAY I LOVE YOU. THE LOOK UPON YOUR FACE SHOWS NO SURPRISE BABY, GUESS YOU ALWAYS KNEW WHEN THINGS PLAYED ON MY MIND, I BELIEVE IN SECOND CHANCES, I BELIEVE IN LOVE FOR LIFE, I BELIEVE YOU CAN MAYBE LOSE LOVE ONCE BUT NEVER TWICE. THROW THE PAST ASIDE, LET'S MAKE UP FOR LOST TIME, IF WE LET THIS LOVE PASS BY WE MAY NEVER FIND THESE FEELINGS AGAIN IN OUR LIVES.

EVERYTHING I EVER WANTED

YOU'RE EVERYTHING I EVER WANTED AND MORE, YOU'RE THE GIRL THAT I'VE NEEDED FOR SO LONG, I THINK I'M OLD ENOUGH TO KNOW NOW, THE REASON I FEEL THE WAY I DO NOW, IN MY OWN WORDS THIS LOVE IS SO MEANT TO BE, IT'S IN YOUR EYES EACH TIME YOU'RE LISTENING TO ME, I'M SAYING THINGS I'VE NEVER SAID BEFORE, AND SO NATURALLY I'M COMING BACK FOR MORE, THERE'S A REASON WHY THIS LOVE IS CHANGING MY LIFE. YOU'RE EVERYTHING I EVER WANTED AND MORE, YOU'RE IN MY MIND IN MY HEART IN MY SOUL, EACH TIME I THINK ABOUT REASON, MY WORK, LOSING TIME, I JUST THINK ABOUT YOU AND LEAVE RESPONSIBILITY BEHIND. MY DAY IT OPENS WITH YOUR HEAD ON MY SHOULDER, I LOVE TO KISS, TOUCH, I LOVE TO HOLD YOU, OUR TIME IT MOVES SO FAST, EVERY HOUR'S A SECOND TILL AT LAST, WE WILL SLEEP ONE NIGHT AND THAT NIGHT IS FOREVER. YOU'RE EVERYTHING I EVER WANTED AND MORE, YOU'RE IN MY MIND IN MY HEART IN MY SOUL, EACH TIME I THINK ABOUT REASON, MY WORK, LOSING TIME, I JUST THINK ABOUT YOU AND LEAVE RESPONSIBILITY BEHIND. THERE'S A REASON WHY THIS LOVE IS CHANGING MY LIFE, YOU'RE EVERYTHING I EVER WANTED AND MORE, YOU'RE IN MY MIND IN MY HEART IN MY SOUL, EACH TIME I THINK ABOUT REASON, MY WORK, LOSING TIME, I JUST THINK ABOUT YOU AND LEAVE RESPONSIBILITY BEHIND.

I'M ALWAYS THINKING ABOUT YOU, I WONDER IF YOU CAN TELL, THESE THINGS I'M FEELING INSIDE ME, I KEEP THEM ALL TO MYSELF, SCARED TO SHOW MY TRUE EMOTIONS, DON'T WANT TO LOVE ALONE. 'CAUSE I FALL SO DEEP, YOU NEVER KNOW, HOW FAR I GO, AND I KNOW WHY, HEARTS BEAT, DESPERATELY, I FALL SO DEEP. SOME PEOPLE THINK LOVE IS FOOLISH, WHILE OTHERS THINK IT'S A GAME, I THINK THAT LOVE IS A FIRE, I'M BURNING UP IN YOUR FLAME, I'M SO LOST IN MY EMOTIONS, WANTING YOU EVERMORE. 'CAUSE I FALL SO DEEP, YOU NEVER KNOW, HOW FAR I GO, AND I KNOW WHY, HEARTS BEAT, DESPERATELY, I FALL SO DEEP. I FALL SO DEEP, AND I'VE COME SO CLOSE TO THE PART, WHERE I REVEAL MY HEART TO YOU, BUT I LOSE MY NERVE, CAN'T FIND THE WORDS, TO TELL YOU THAT IT'S TRUE. I FALL SO DEEP, 'CAUSE I FALL SO DEEP, YOU NEVER KNOW, HOW FAR I GO, AND I KNOW WHY, HEARTS BEAT, DESPERATELY, I FALL SO DEEP. I FALL SO DEEP, I FALL SO DEEP, I FALL SO DEEP, I FALL SO DEEP.

I FALL SO DEEP

LAY DOWN FOR LOVE

I WAS ALONE WITH YOU ON MY MIND, LOOK AT ME NOW YOU'VE LEFT ME BEHIND, YOU'RE ALL THAT MATTERS, YOU ARE MY LIFE, YOU ARE THE ONE THAT SHOULD BE HERE BY MY SIDE, YOU ARE MY LOVER, YOU SHOULD BE MY FRIEND, DON'T YOU THINK WE'VE GOT SOME TALKING TO DO?, ONLY LOVE DEPENDS ON YOU. DON'T TELL ME IT'S OVER WHEN IT'S NOT OVER YET, DON'T TELL ME YOU LOVE ME WHEN YOU'RE TRYN'A THROW THIS LOVE AWAY, DON'T SAY I'VE CHANGED GIRL BECAUSE CHANGE IS NOT ENOUGH, DON'T SAY THAT IT'S OVER WHEN YOU KNOW THAT WE CAN FIGHT IT YOU KNOW, WE'VE GOTTA LAY DOWN FOR LOVE. WHERE IS YOUR KISS, WHERE IS YOUR TOUCH, THE TASTE OF YOUR LIPS, I MISS IT SO MUCH, YOU SAID YOU'D BE BACK SOON, YOU SAID YOU'D BE HERE, YOU SEEM TO RUN EVERY TIME LOVE COMES NEAR, REMEMBER WHEN WE WERE LOVERS, REMEMBER WHEN WE WERE FRIENDS, DON'T YOU THINK WE'VE GOT SOME TALKING TO DO?, IN THE END IT'S UP TO YOU. DON'T TELL ME IT'S OVER WHEN IT'S NOT OVER YET, DON'T TELL ME YOU LOVE ME WHEN YOU'RE TRYN'A THROW THIS LOVE AWAY, DON'T SAY I'VE CHANGED GIRL BECAUSE CHANGE IS NOT ENOUGH, DON'T SAY THAT IT'S OVER WHEN YOU KNOW THAT WE CAN FIGHT IT YOU KNOW, WE'VE GOTTA LAY DOWN FOR LOVE. LAY DOWN FOR ME, LAY DOWN FOR YOU, LAY DOWN FOR EVERYTHING YOU DO, 'CAUSE YOU KNOW ITS RIGHT, YOU KNOW IT'S TIME, TO LOVE ME FOR THE REST OF YOUR LIFE, EVEN WHEN YOU' GOT GOOD LIFE IT AIN'T EASY, EVEN WHEN YOU' GOT GOOD LOVE IT AIN'T RIGHT, ALL YOU GOTTA' DO IS LOVE ME TO PLEASE ME, AND I'LL BE RIGHT BESIDE YOU FOR LIFE. DON'T TELL ME IT'S OVER WHEN IT'S NOT OVER YET, DON'T TELL ME YOU LOVE ME WHEN YOU'RE TRYN'A THROW THIS LOVE AWAY, DON'T SAY I'VE CHANGED GIRL BECAUSE CHANGE IS NOT ENOUGH, DON'T SAY THAT IT'S OVER WHEN YOU KNOW THAT WE CAN FIGHT IT YOU KNOW, WE'VE GOTTA LAY DOWN FOR LOVE.

FOREVER LOVE

LOVE IT HAS SO MANY BEAUTIFUL FACES SHARING LIVES AND SHARING DAYS, MY LOVE IT HAD SO MANY EMPTY SPACES, I'M SHARING A MEMORY HOPE THAT'S HOW IT STAYS, NOW I'M DEEP INSIDE LOVE AND STILL BREATHING, SHE IS HOLDING MY HEART IN HER HAND, I'M THE CLOSEST I'VE BEEN TO BELIEVING THIS COULD BE LOVE FOREVER, ALL THROUGHOUT MY LIFE THE REASONS I'VE DEMANDED, BUT HOW CAN I REASON WITH THE REASON I'M A MAN. IN A MINUTE I'M NEEDING TO HOLD HER, IN AN HOUR I'M COLD, COLD AS STONE, WHEN SHE LEAVES IT GETS HARDER AND HARDER TO FACE LIFE ALONE, NOW MY DREAMS ARE FILLED WITH TIMES WHEN WE'RE TOGETHER, GUESS WHAT I NEED FROM HER IS FOREVER LOVE.

NEVER KNEW

I FOUND THE ROAD TO NOWHERE, THE GREENER GRASS IT TURNED TO STONE, YOUR SHADOWED FACE SHINES A RAINBOW NOW, THE SIGN I FOUND IT POINTED HOME. NEVER KNEW THAT I'D MISS YOU THIS WAY, NEVER KNEW THAT PAIN COULD SURVIVE HERE INSIDE, NEVER KNEW THAT I'D MISS YOU THIS MUCH, I'M REACHING OUT TO TOUCH, I'M CALLING OUT FOR LOVE. I ONLY WALKED TO BREATHE AGAIN, I FELT THE WALLS WERE FALLING DOWN, CAUGHT A BUSY TRAIN TO FREEDOM, NOW HERE I STAND IN THIS LONELY TOWN. NEVER KNEW THAT I'D MISS YOU THIS WAY, NEVER KNEW THAT PAIN COULD SURVIVE HERE INSIDE, NEVER KNEW THAT I'D MISS YOU THIS MUCH, I'M REACHING OUT TO TOUCH, I'M CALLING OUT FOR LOVE. AND WHEN STARS FILL THE SKY IT TAKES ME BACK TO THE TIME, WHEN WE LIVED FOR ONLY LOVE, ONLY LOVE, ONLY LOVE, THAT I FEEL FOR YOU. NEVER KNEW THAT I'D MISS YOU THIS WAY, NEVER KNEW THAT PAIN COULD SURVIVE HERE INSIDE, NEVER KNEW THAT I'D MISS YOU THIS MUCH, I'M REACHING OUT TO TOUCH, I'M CALLING OUT FOR LOVE.

OPEN ROAD

MY LIFE IS EXTRAORDINARY BARE, I FOUGHT THE FEAR AND CHASED THE PAIN, MY LIFE DOESN'T NEED TO BE EXPLAINED, I CHOSE TO WALK THIS LIFE AS ONE. SOMETIMES AS I LIVE UPON MY ISLAND, CUT OFF FROM EMOTION AND IT'S PAIN, THAT'S WHEN I AM TEMPTED BY THE WATERS, THE WATERS THAT CAN TAKE ME FAR AWAY. SO I'LL JUST KEEP ON WALKING DOWN THIS OPEN ROAD, HOPING SOMEONE SOMEWHERE NEEDS ME, SO I'LL JUST KEEP ON WALKING DOWN THIS OPEN ROAD, TALKING TO THE MAN WHO KNOWS ME, YES HE KNOWS ME, THE MAN IS ME. MY LIFE WAS ONCE FULL OF PEOPLE'S FACES, BROUGHT TO ME BY LOVE WHICH ISN'T STRANGE, MY LIFE HAD THE GOODNESS OF BLUE WATERS, A DAYS A DAY FOR ALL I USED TO SAY. SOMETIMES I CAN SIT AND CRY MY HEART OUT, DROWNING IN MY AUTOCRATIC WAYS, THAT'S WHEN I AM TEMPTED BY THE WATERS, THE WATERS THAT CAN TAKE ME FAR AWAY. SO I'LL JUST KEEP ON WALKING DOWN THIS OPEN ROAD, HOPING SOMEONE SOMEWHERE NEEDS ME, SO I'LL JUST KEEP ON WALKING DOWN THIS OPEN ROAD, TALKING TO THE MAN WHO KNOWS ME, YES HE KNOWS ME, THE MAN IS ME. MY LIFE IS NOW FULL OF PEOPLE'S FACES, WITHIN THE LIGHT OF CHANGE I PULLED AWAY, MY LIFE SHOWS THAT 'NO MAN IS AN ISLAND', I'VE EXCHANGED THE PIECE OF LIFE I CUT AWAY. NOW YOU WON'T SEE ME WALKING DOWN THAT OPEN ROAD, I'VE FOUND SOMEONE NOW WHO NEEDS ME, NO YOU WON'T SEE ME WALKING DOWN THAT OPEN ROAD, I'VE FOUND AT LAST THE MAN WHO KNOWS ME, YES HE KNOWS ME, THE MAN WAS ME, THE MAN WAS ME.

I HAVE BEEN LIVING, I HAVE BEEN FOOLED, I HAVE BEEN MANY THINGS BUT I'VE ALWAYS BEEN IN LOVE WITH YOU, I HAVE BEEN TRAVELLING, EATING LIFE'S FOOD, THOUGH I'VE BEEN FAR AWAY, I HAVE STILL REMAINED IN LOVE WITH YOU. I'VE BEEN GIVEN A CHANCE TO SHARE MY MUSIC WITH THE WORLD, SOON MY SONG WILL BE OVER, 'TILL I SING THE SONG OF LOVE, FOR ME AND YOU, I'VE BEEN SHARING WITH THE WORLD MY SONGS OF LOVE. WELL BABY I HAVE BEEN LEARNING, I HAVE BEEN USED, I HAVE BEEN SHELTERING WITHIN THIS PLENTY WORLD OF LOVE I SHARE WITH YOU, I'VE BEEN GIVEN THE ANSWER, I'VE BEEN GIVEN WORDS OF LOVE, I'VE BEEN GIVEN THE REASON, AND THE REASON I'VE BEEN SHARING WITH THE WORLD, I'VE BEEN SHARING WITH THE WORLD MY SONGS OF LOVE, THAT'S WHY I'LL ALWAYS BE IN LOVE, I WILL ALWAYS BE IN LOVE, I WILL ALWAYS BE IN LOVE WITH YOU, ALWAYS BE IN LOVE, I WILL ALWAYS BE IN LOVE, I WILL ALWAYS BE IN LOVE WITH YOU.

ALWAYS

LOVE WONT WAIT

Words and Music by
Shep Pettibone and Madonna Louise Ciccone

When I first saw your face, knew that I could not
So here I am with my heart on my sleeve, you said 'Ba-by, put your

he-si-tate. You said 'Ba-by don't go too fast,
trust in me.' But I have come to the end of the line,

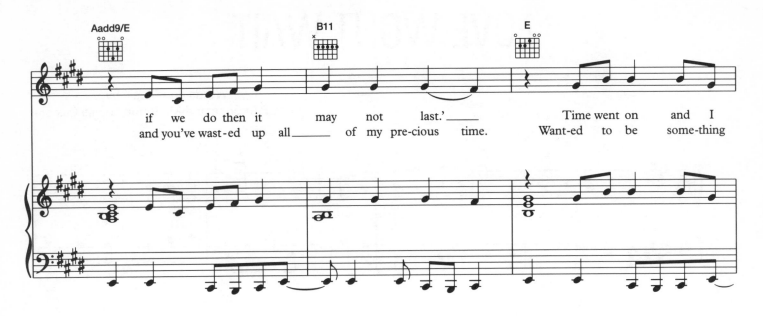

if we do then it may not last.' _____ Time went on and I
and you've wast-ed up all _____ of my pre-cious time. Want-ed to be some-thing

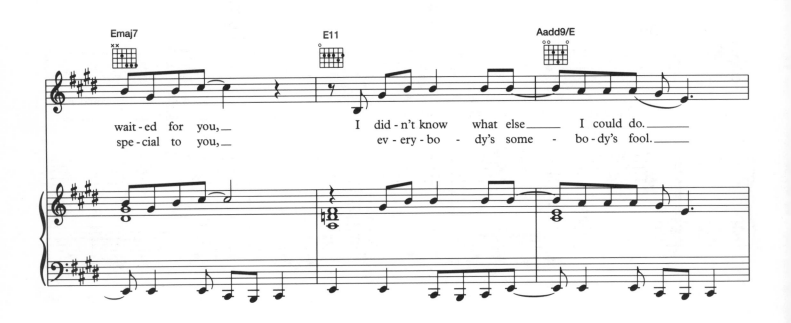

wait-ed for you, _ I did-n't know what else _____ I could do. _____
spe-cial to you, _ ev-ery-bo - dy's some - bo-dy's fool. _____

I thought that we'd al-ways be _____ to - geth - er,
Won't be your fool, no you've got _____ me all wrong,

you said 'Hold on, it just____ gets bet - ter.'
you won't know what you had____ till it's gone.____

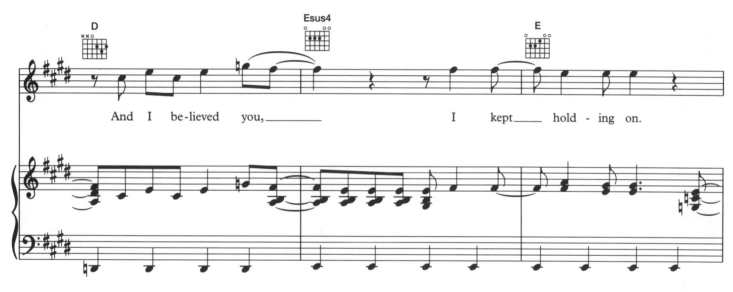

And I be-lieved you,_____ I kept____ hold - ing on.

You think that I could nev - er leave you,_____ you think I'm

15

SO HELP ME GIRL

Words and Music by
Howard Perdew and Andrew Spooner

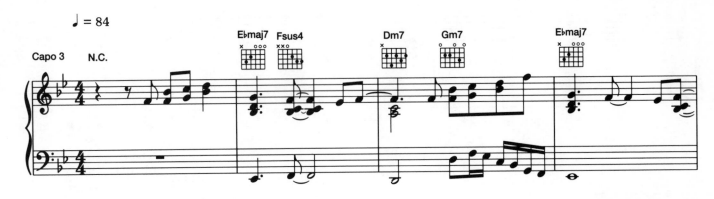

You could have kissed me like this was-n't gon - na last,_____
You had to be____ there un - til the sun___ came up,_____

kept me from say - ing some-thing I'll ne - ver take back._____
mak-ing last night___ feel like a vi - sion of things yet to come._____
You

MY COMMITMENT

Words and Music by
Gary Barlow and Diane Warren

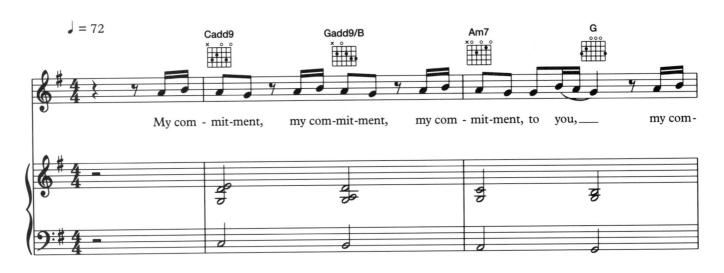

My com-mit-ment, my com-mit-ment, my com-mit-ment, to you,___ my com-

-mit-ment, my com-mit-ment is to live to love you. ___ I will hold you, I will show you you can

put your faith in me,___ all of my_ life___ I'll be_ all that you need.

HANG ON IN THERE BABY

Words and Music by
Johnny Bristol

What's that now ba - by, what's that you say?__ Some-thing is eat-ing at__ you and it's a-

-bout to get__ a - way.____ Don't fight__ it ba - by, you bet - ter

Are You Ready Now

Words and Music by
Gary Barlow

share to-night the years we've been a-part___ ba - by, from the time we said good-bye_ un - til now.

How the nights we laughed and loved still feel like yes-ter-day,

Can we

EVERYTHING I EVER WANTED

Words and Music by
Gary Barlow

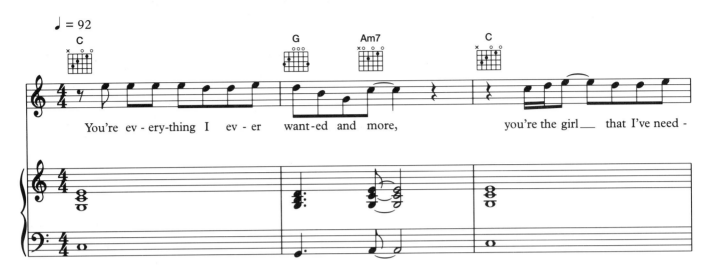

You're ev-ery-thing I ev-er want-ed and more, you're the girl___ that I've need-

-ed for so long,___ I think I'm old e-nough to know___ now, the

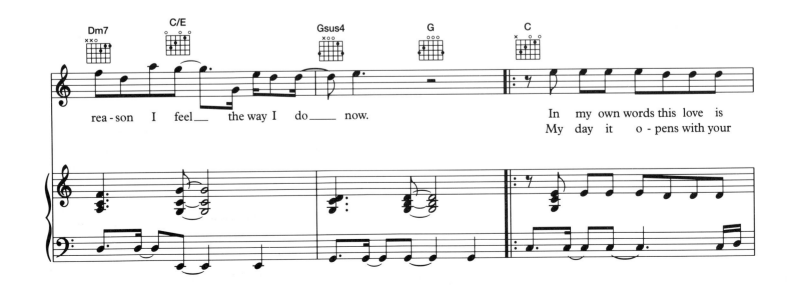

rea-son I feel___ the way I do___ now.
My day it o-pens with your

In my own words this love is

I Fall So Deep

Words and Music by
Larry Loftin and Amy Powers

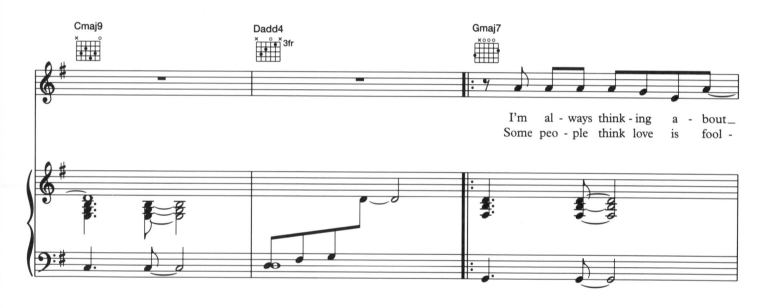

I'm al - ways think - ing a - bout_
Some peo - ple think love is fool -

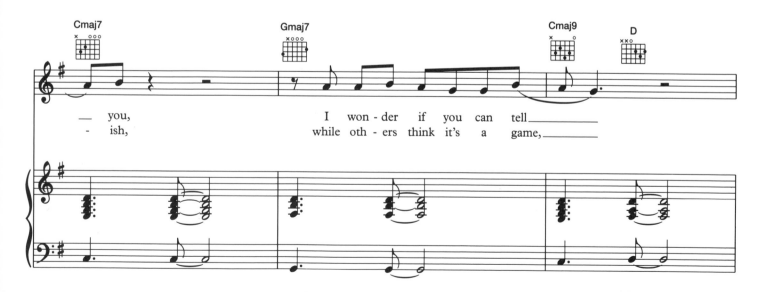

_ you,   I won - der if you can tell_____
- ish,   while oth - ers think it's a game,_____

LAY DOWN FOR LOVE

Words and Music by
Gary Barlow, Richard Stannard
and Matthew Rowbottom

53

FOREVER LOVE

Words and Music by
Gary Barlow

NEVER KNEW

Words and Music by
Gary Barlow

love, oh,_____ and when stars fill the sky,_____ it takes me back

to the time, when we lived for on - ly love.

Ne - ver

OPEN ROAD

Words and Music by
Gary Barlow

My life is ex - tra - ord - in - ary bare,___

My life was once full of peo - ple's fa - ces,

ALWAYS

Words and Music by
Gary Barlow

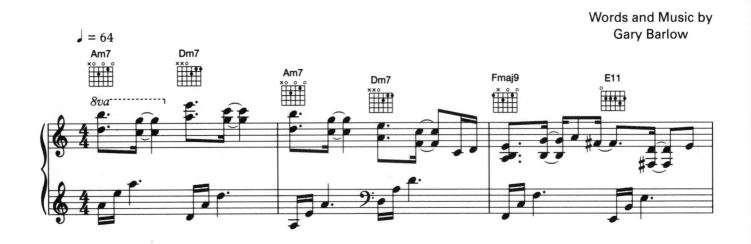

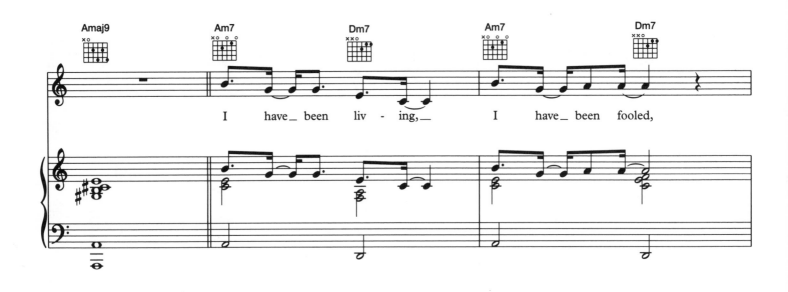

I have_ been liv - ing,_ I have_ been fooled,

I have been ma - ny things, but I've al - ways been in love_ with you,___